THREE CLARINET PICTURES

1
SUMMER LANDSCAPE

MICHAEL JACQUES

AB 2186

2
STILL LIFE

THREE CLARINET PICTURES
1
SUMMER LANDSCAPE

CLARINET in B♭

MICHAEL JACQUES

AB 2186

2
STILL LIFE

3
STREET SCENE

3
STREET SCENE

Processed and printed by
Halstan & Co. Ltd., Amersham, Bucks., England